GOAT

COLORING BOOK FOR KIDS

PLUS BONUS ACTIVITY PAGES!

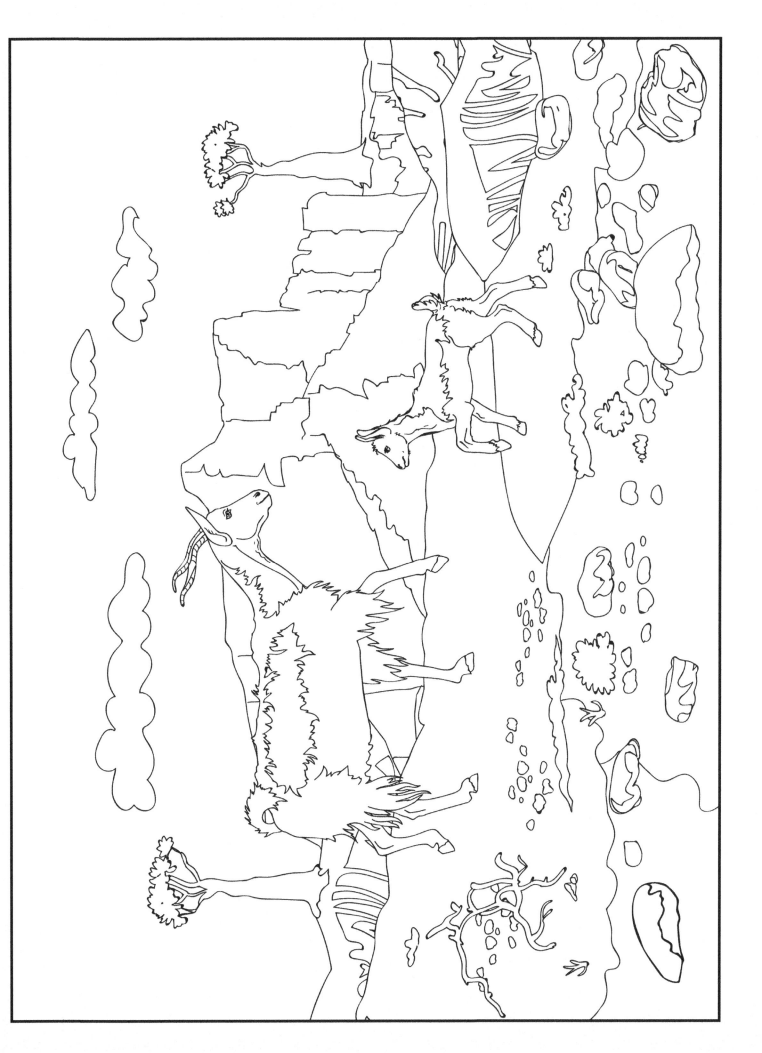

BONUS
ACTIVITY
PAGES

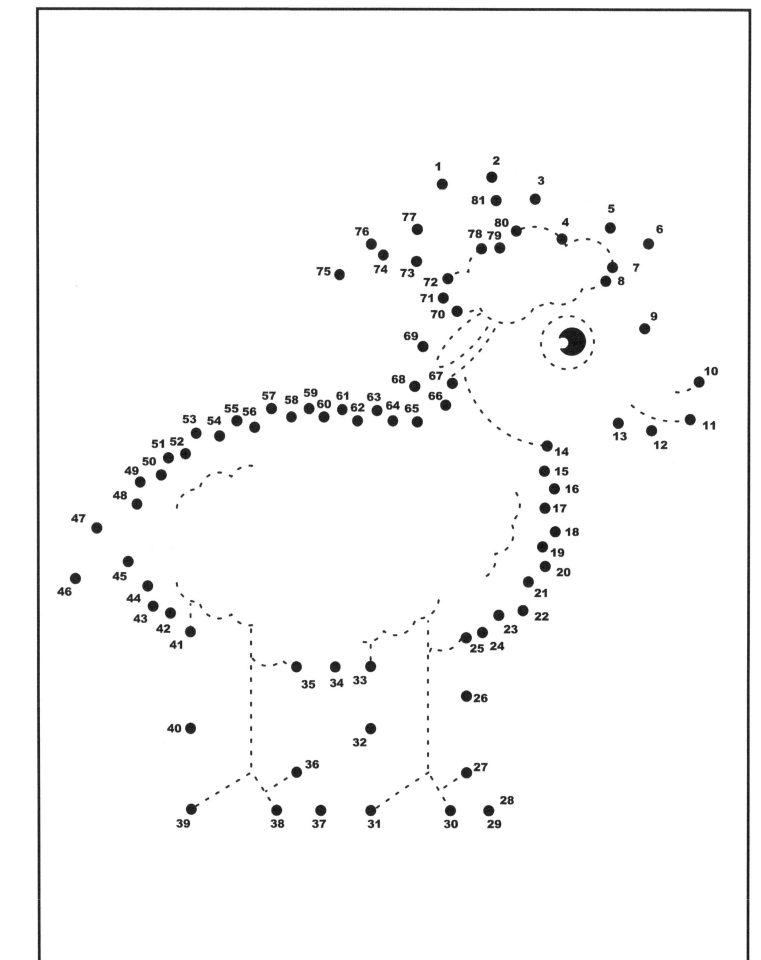

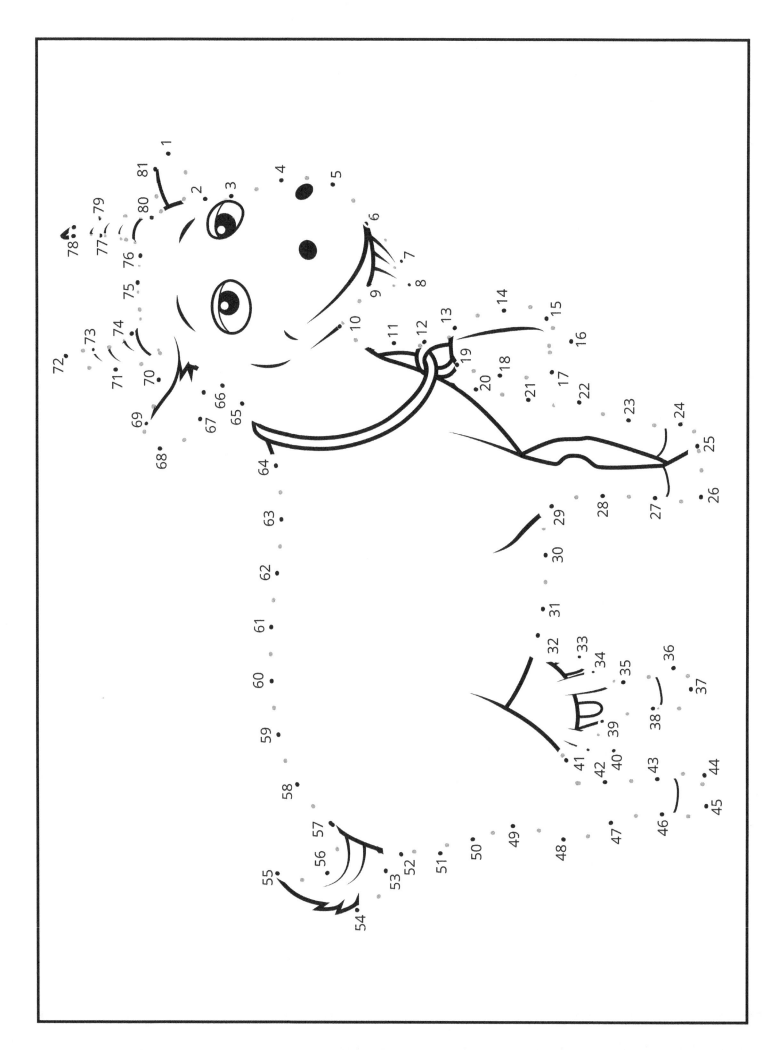

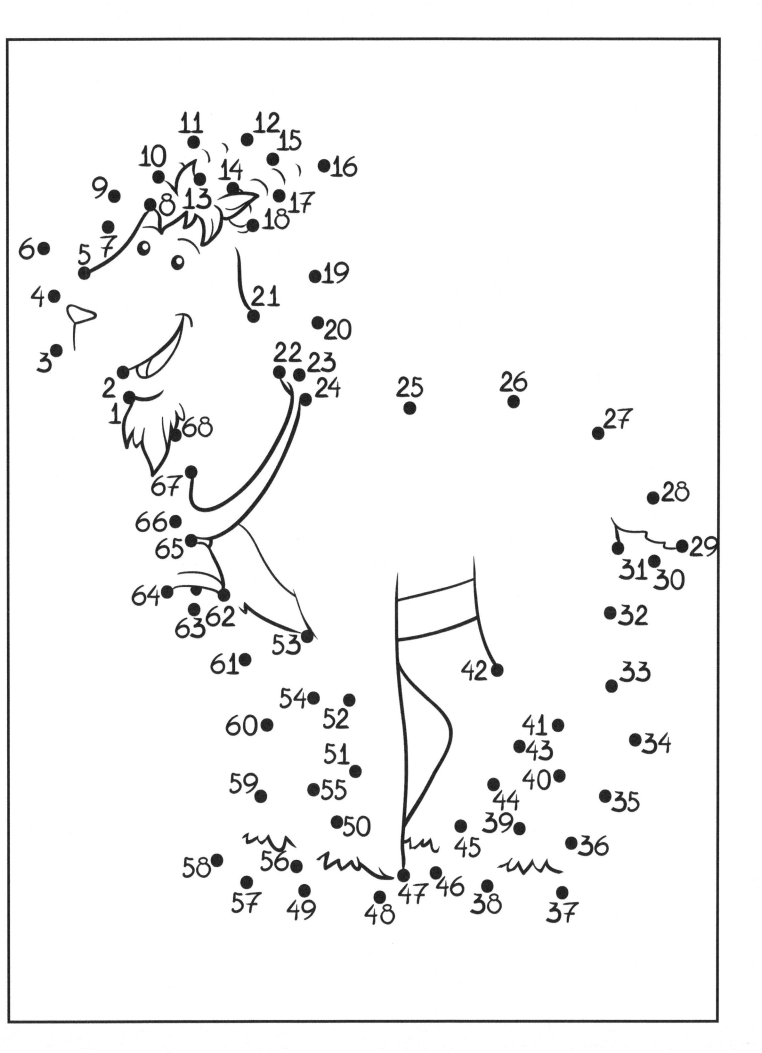

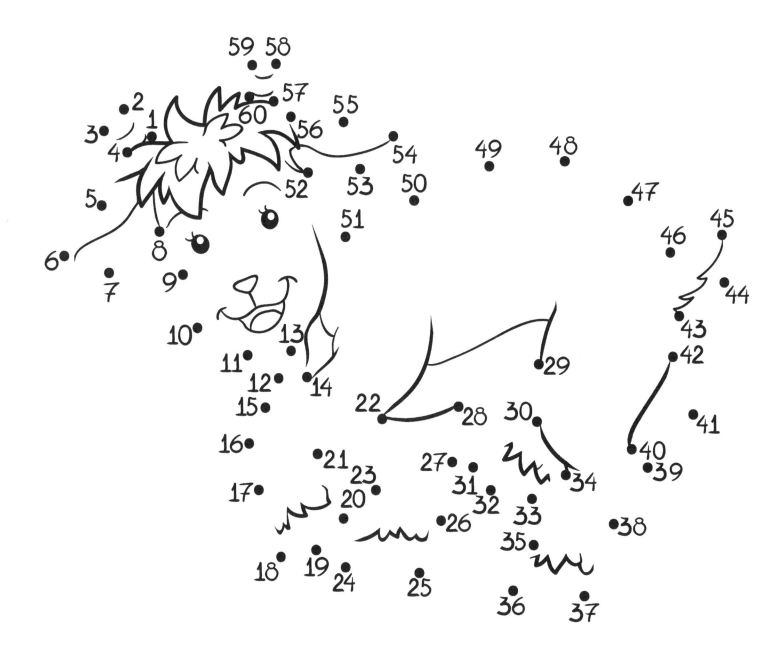

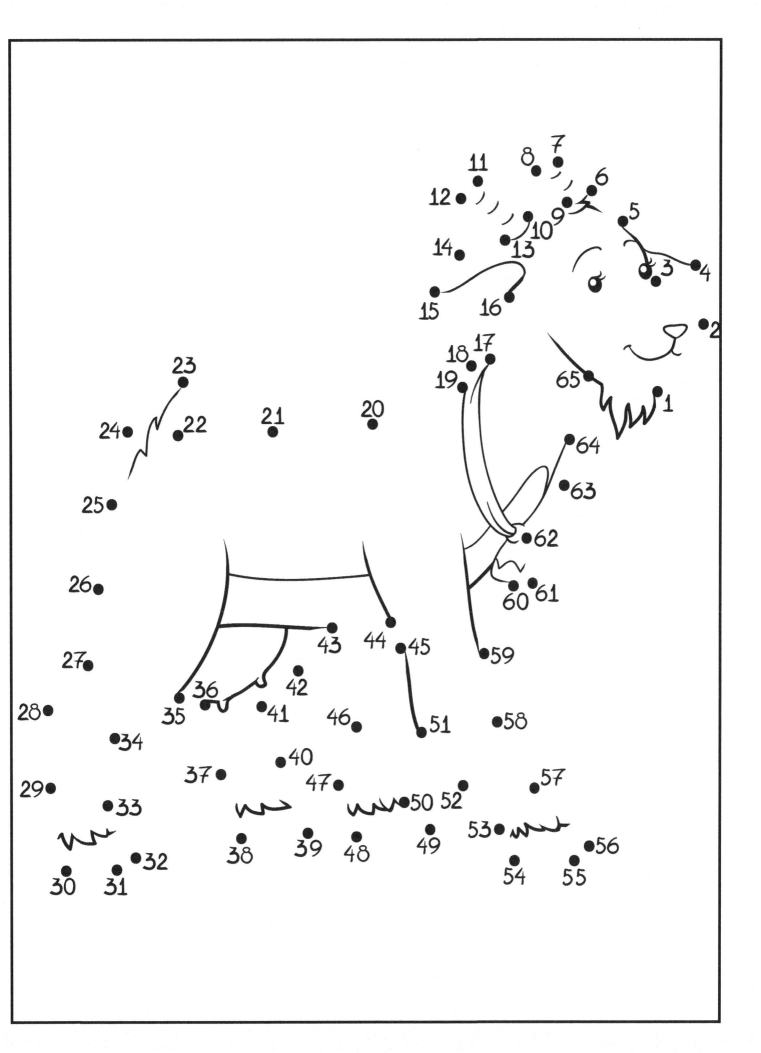

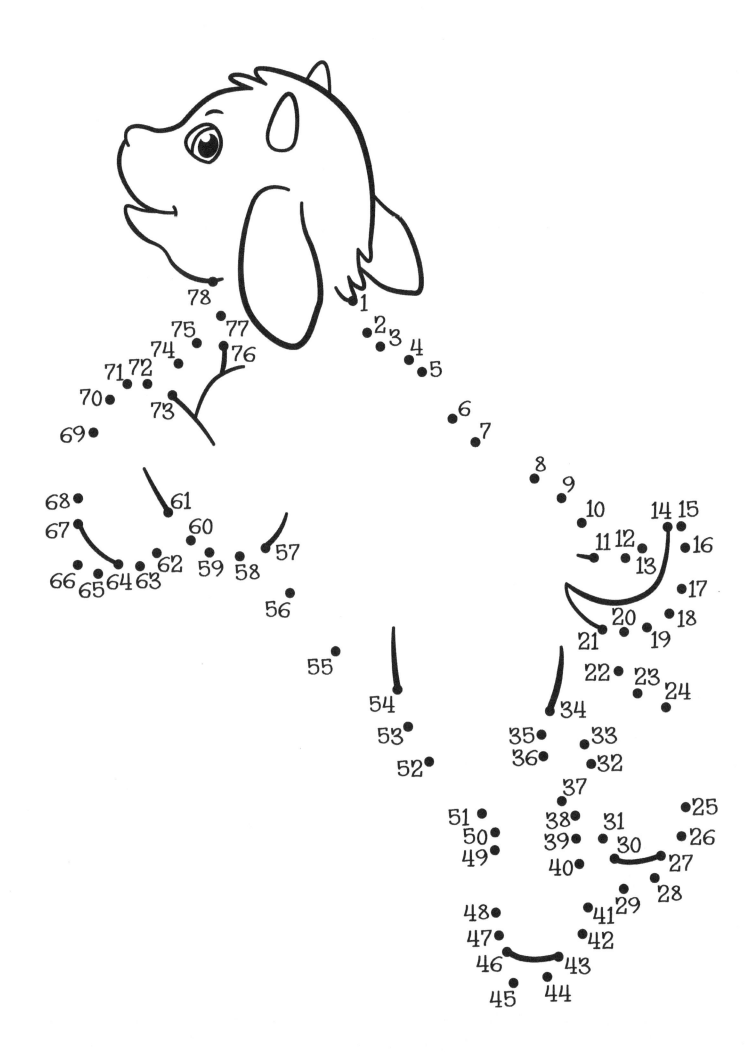

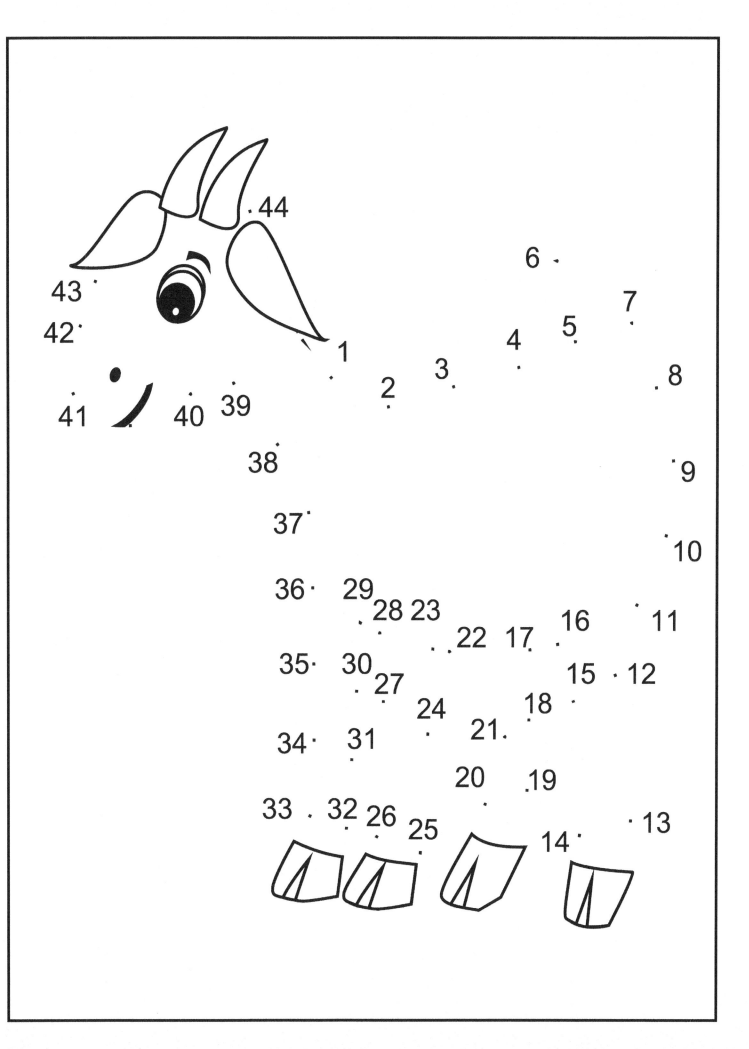

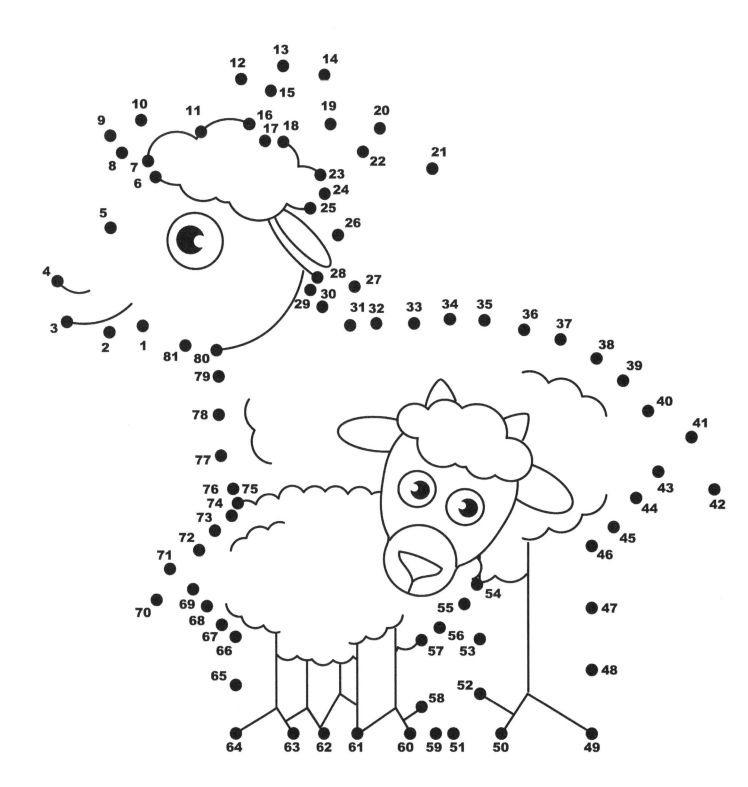

Copy the Picture Using the Grid

Copy the Picture Using the Grid

Your Turn to Draw

Your Turn to Draw

Your Turn to Draw

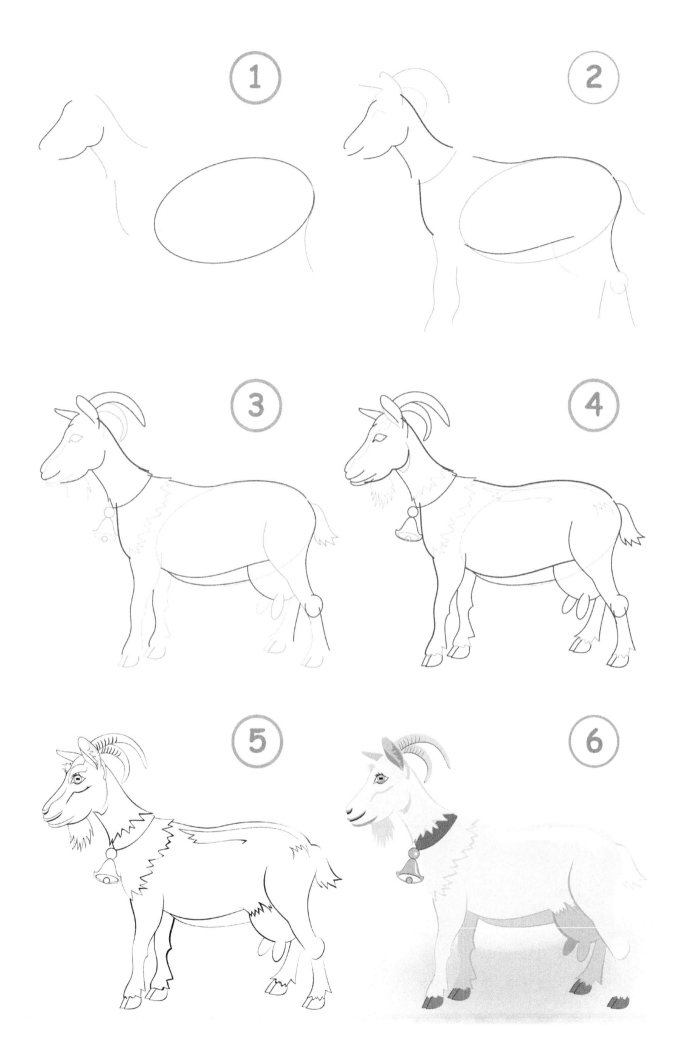

Your Turn to Draw

let's help the mother goat
to find her cub

Let's help the mother goat
to find her cub

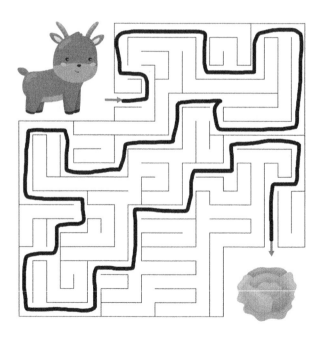

Find 10 Differences Between the Two Pictures

Find 7 Differences Between the Two Pictures

1. Cat 2. Cow 3. Duck 4. Chicken
5. Goat 6. Rooster 7. Turkey 8. Horse
9. Pig 10. Dog 11. Sheep

Answer: COUNTRYSIDE

Made in United States
North Haven, CT
14 July 2022

21380318R00063